COMPACTS are very different from every other type of adventure game book. They have been specially designed so that their play is as convenient as possible.

The special fold-out flap at the front of the book has all your *game accessories*. Within the fold-out flap at the back are all your *score cards*. This means that whenever you have to amend your score card, it can always be located immediately.

The only thing you have to provide yourself is a pen or pencil. You don't even need an eraser because there are enough score cards (a whole 30!) to allow for a fresh one to be used for each new game.

COMPACTS are ideal for playing at home, on holiday, in the car . . .

D1638657

STEPHEN THRAVES
COMPACT
ADVENTURE GAME BOOKS

GHOST RIDE!

Illustrated by Peter Dennis

HODDER AND STOUGHTON
LONDON SYDNEY AUCKLAND

British Library Cataloguing in Publication Data

A catalogue record for this book is available from the British Library

ISBN 0 340 60680 0

Text copyright © Stephen Thraves 1994
Concept copyright © Stephen Thraves 1993
Format copyright © Stephen Thraves 1993
Illustrations copyright © Peter Dennis 1994

First published 1994

The rights of Stephen Thraves to be identified as the author of the text
of this work and of Peter Dennis to be identified as the illustrator of this
work have been asserted by them in accordance with the Copyright,
Designs and Patents Act 1988.

Published by Hodder and Stoughton Children's Books,
a division of Hodder Headline plc,
338 Euston Road, London NW1 3BH

Photoset by Rowland Phototypesetting Ltd,
Bury St Edmunds, Suffolk

Printed and bound in Great Britain by
BPCC Hazell Books Ltd
Member of BPCC Ltd

Where are you going to find a great news story? As one of the school newspaper's chief journalists, you've often asked yourself that before, of course. But the newspaper's next issue is being entered for the national 'School Newspaper of the Year' competition. So this time the story has to be better than ever!

Well, the town hall isn't much help – the only events they've organised for the forthcoming week are an art exhibition and an outdoor violin concert! Nor is the local police station; they tell you life is especially quiet at the moment, not an intriguing case for months . . .

Growing desperate, you pay a visit to the nearest tourist information office, some ten miles away. Any new theme parks to be opened in this part of the country, any historical pageants about to take place? Not in the next few days, apparently. Just as you're frustratedly leaving the tourist information office, though, a small brochure catches your eye.

It's entitled *GHOST RIDE!*

Curious, you open the brochure and see that it's an invitation to take an evening round-trip on the *Dark Valley Railway*. The brochure tells you that the steam-train service through Dark Valley ceased operating some forty years ago because of declining demand in this remote area. But a group of railway enthusiasts have recently restored the line, and at weekends have been providing steam-train journeys for tourists.

GHOST RIDE!, explains the brochure, is to be a

special *evening* journey on 15th June. Before the line closed, apparently, a guard on one of the trains claimed that every year, on 15th June, he would encounter ghosts during the evening round-trip. His name was Walter Potts and he said that the ghosts would always appear at exactly the same times and places; some a short distance from the railway line, some *next to* the railway line and some even at the train's windows!

Realising that 15th June is only a couple of days away, you decide that this will be your news story. Armed with your Polaroid camera, you'll travel on the *Ghost Ride*. You don't expect to snap any *real* ghosts, of course, but you should come back with some great photographs. At any rate, they should at least be a bit more interesting than pictures of a violin concert!

Whether it's expecting ghosts or not, 15th June certainly starts very ominously. You wake to heavy rain and a brooding sky. The downpour continues throughout the day; the sky growing more and more menacing as evening approaches. While cycling the fifteen miles or so to Dark Valley, you wonder just how many other people are going to be braving the elements to join you on the train.

It looks as if there will be even fewer than you thought. You have about a mile to go to the station at the start of the railway line – Bleakwood station – when you find that part of the road has been badly flooded. By walking with your bike along the road's steep bank, *you* can just about reach the other side of the floodwater. But surely no car could do so!

Finally approaching the desolate little station, you have your worst fears confirmed. There's not a single vehicle in the station's car park. With sunken heart, you look for the station's ticket office. You very much doubt that there will be anyone there. Even if there is, he's bound to tell you that the special train journey has been cancelled.

To your great delight, you find that you're wrong on both accounts. There *is* someone in the ticket office; a man with a pencil behind his ear. And he says that having advertised the special trip, they're determined that it should still run – plenty of passengers or not.

But should you be so delighted? For, as you stand on the rain-soaked platform, waiting for the steam train to emerge from its grim shed, you discover that you're not merely one of a few passengers – you're the *only* passenger!

You make another worrying discovery. Checking your pocket, you find that all your spare rolls of film seem to have fallen out. This must have occurred when you were walking along that steep bank; you did slip a couple of times on the soaking grass. So the only photos available to you are those still unexposed in your camera – and there are only SIX!

Perhaps, for these two reasons, you shouldn't make the train journey after all. But what if there really are ghosts to be snapped? Your school newspaper would be an absolute sensation. So surely, however scary the trip might be, you'd be mad to miss out on such an opportunity . . .

◇ GAME INSTRUCTIONS ◇

1. For each attempt at the game, you must use one of the 30 score cards within the fold-out flap at the *back* of the book.
2. The 📷 column on your score card is for showing the *number of photographs you have left*, the 👻 column the *number of times you have snapped a ghost on a photograph* and the 🎒 column which *accessories* you have collected during the game.

📷 Column

3. At the start of the game you have **6** photographs in your Polaroid camera. Every time you take a photograph (either intentionally or by accident) during the game, you must reduce this score by one. You do this by using a pen or pencil to delete the top number showing in the 📷 column. So, for the first photograph you take, delete the **6**, for the second photograph the **5** . . . and so on.
4. When you have deleted every number down to and including **1**, it means that your film has run out and so you cannot continue with your adventure. If you wish to make another attempt at the game, you must start all over again from the beginning (using a fresh score card).

👻 Column

5. If one of the photographs you take shows a ghost, then you must also mark the 👻 column on your

score card. For your first ghost photograph circle the **1** in that column, for the second circle the **2**, and so on.

6. Many of the photographs you take, however, won't show a ghost at all. You might *think* that you're snapping a ghost but when you turn to the paragraph that shows how the photo develops a few seconds later, you'll often be disappointed. When carefully studied, the 'ghost' might merely prove to be a sheep grazing in the dusk, the white sails of a distant windmill . . . or simply steam from the train!

7. The more times you attempt the game, though, the more skilful you'll become at working out where and when to use your camera. So your 🔲 score should become better and better.

8. Your ultimate aim is to take the maximum of **6** photographs showing ghosts. Only **6** clear ghost photographs will categorically *prove* that the railway line is genuinely haunted . . . and ensure that your newspaper takes that coveted 'School Newspaper of the Year' award!

🐾 Column

9. There are three useful *accessories* to be picked up during the game: Walter Potts's Map (which shows ghost appearances a short distance from the railway line), an old Newspaper (which describes

ghost appearances right next to the railway line) and Walter Potts's Timetable (which lists ghost appearances actually at the train's windows). These three accessories are depicted on the fold-out flap at the *front* of the book.

10. Possession of these accessories will greatly improve your chances of succeeding at the adventure and so you should make every effort to find them during the game.

11. If you *do* pick up one of the accessories, show this on your score card by circling that accessory's initial (M = Map, N = Newspaper, T = Timetable) in the 📖 column. This means that you are then entitled to *consult* this particular accessory where appropriate during the game.

12. Any accessory not circled in your score card must NOT be consulted at any point during the game.

*To start this exciting
journey, turn the page . . .*

You again peer through the heavy rain towards the engine shed at the far end of the platform. There's still no sign of anything emerging from its dark interior. A few puffs of steam waft out once in a while but they are yet to be followed by a hissing engine. So you decide to explore this antiquated little station. Everything seems to be exactly as it was in Walter Potts's time, all those years ago. The original gas-lamps stand along the platform, the type that were lit and doused by long poles, and old-fashioned advertisements are half-peeling from the walls. You come to the dark window of a tiny waiting-room and you wonder whether you should step inside. Or perhaps you should enter the equally tiny tea room just beyond it? Or keep strolling right to the end of the platform and investigate the old water tank there . . .

If enter waiting-room	*go to 140*
If enter tea room	*go to 53*
If investigate water tank	*go to 117*

2

Leaning out of the window, you see that a young tree has come down in the storm and is lying right across the line! Ted is helping the train's driver and stoker to lift it clear – but it looks hard work and so you decide to offer to help. You leap down from your carriage and run up to the panting trio. **Go to 32.**

3

You've just made yourself comfortable in this second class compartment (or, at least, as comfortable as the hard seats will allow!) when the train starts pulling out of the station. It gradually picks up speed, screeching and rattling against the thunder which occasionally crashes all round it. You check your watch to see what time it is now . . . **Go to 132.**

4

You point your camera all the way along the corridor and lean against one of the exit doors so you're nice and steady when the train starts moving again. But you didn't close this door properly when you stepped into the carriage . . . and you suddenly tumble back out of it on to the embankment! It's lucky that the train is still stationary or your injuries could have been much worse than light bruises. You've still been taught quite a lesson, though, for although you weren't really hurt, you couldn't help knocking your camera's shutter-release button as you landed. You've lost a precious photograph!

Delete the top number in your score card's 📷 column. Go next to 154.

5

As the train edges towards the little signal box, you're sure you've made the right choice. You think you can see something *moving* behind its dark windows! But are you becoming excited for nothing? It's probably just the reflection of the train as it jerks past the windows.

Your own carriage now reaches the signal box, though, and your excitement returns. Isn't that a pale face at the window? Knowing that such apparitions can often be much clearer when studied in a photograph, you quickly raise your camera. But what if that pale face is merely a reflection of yourself?

If take photo   *go to 47*
If not   *go to 24*

Well done – it was a ghost! Record this in the 🖼 *column of your score card. Also, delete the top number in the* 📷 *column to deduct the photo used. Go next to 24.*

The train now reaches the other side of the forbidding valley and, as on the outward journey, you breathe a long sigh of relief. Coming up in the next five minutes or so should be Littleoak station again. So you can work out what time this would be, you check your watch. The time now is just coming up to ten past nine. You then notice something rather strange about your watch. The second-hand seems to be trembling slightly as it moves round! Is this because ten past nine is when a ghost is due to appear at the windows of this first class carriage?

*If you have circled the **T** in your score card's* 📖
*column, you may consult the **TIMETABLE** access-*
ory now to find out if a ghost will appear at this
carriage at this time. If not, you'll have to take a risk:
    Watch windows   **go to 27**
    Don't bother watching here   **go to 85**

While you're standing on the footbridge the rain suddenly becomes much heavier again. You therefore dash back towards the train. By the time you reach it, huge sheets of rain are already sweeping across the deserted little station. The thunder starts up again as well, even more ferocious than before. You're relieved to see that the lights are still on in the carriages – for the last part of this trip is clearly going to be the most

frightening of all! You quickly consider which carriage
you should travel in for this final part of the journey.

Observation car   **go to 19**
First class carriage   **go to 88**
Second class carriage   **go to 67**

9

You at last reach the end of the eerie viaduct and you
breathe a sigh of relief as the train starts to pick up speed
once more. Sinister Dark Valley is safely behind you
again! It shouldn't be long now before the train pulls
into Littleoak station. You glance at your watch and see
that it's very nearly ten minutes past nine. You wonder
if this is a likely time for a ghost to appear at the
observation car's broad windows!

If you have circled the T in your score card's 📖
column, you may consult the TIMETABLE access-

ory now to find out if a ghost will appear at this carriage at this time. If not, you'll have to take a risk:

Watch windows   *go to 141*
Don't bother watching yet   *go to 85*

10

It was just a scarecrow! **Delete the top number in your score card's  column. Go next to 105.**

11

'Suit yourself,' Ted mumbles when you tell him that you prefer to remain in the observation car for the moment. 'But don't build up yer 'opes about seeing any ghosts out of the windows. If I were you, I'd save yer photos for yer next family 'oliday!' You completely ignore Ted's advice, though, and as soon as the grumpy guard has left your carriage, you check that your camera is all ready for taking a photograph! *Go to 90.*

12

You pull down one of the old, rattling windows in this corridor and point your camera towards the large clump of trees. Their branches are certainly swaying about a good deal in this strong wind – but there's not yet any sign of anything *unnatural* amongst them! You're watching the trees gradually recede into the darkness when suddenly you feel something touch your shoulder. You start trembling, not daring to turn round. Has a ghost actually *boarded* the train? *Go next to 151.*

13

You quickly step out into the corridor so you'll be on the right side for when you pass the water tank. Your haste wasn't really needed, though, for the train's now moving so slowly that the water tank is still quite a way off. And when it does finally come closer, it can't be seen very well anyway because it becomes enveloped by all the engine's steam! You nevertheless point your camera at the clouds of steam, ready for when they waft away from the tank. Perhaps it's *then* that a ghost will finally be revealed. *Go to 81.*

Your photograph shows that it *was* a skeleton at the tunnel entrance – but it's obvious that it's just a toy one. It must have been hung up there to add atmosphere to the *ghost ride*! **Delete the top number in your score card's 📷 column. Go next to 28.**

15

Since you're so concerned about how little time you might have left for taking photographs, you immediately start studying the passing scenery through your open window. First, not too far away, you see a shadowy stone obelisk – presumably some sort of monument. Then, just as the obelisk is starting to disappear behind you, that distant manor house comes into view again. Should your camera follow this eerie-looking house? Or should it be quickly pointed back at that obelisk?

If you have circled the M in your score card's  *column, you may study the MAP accessory now to find out if a ghost is due to appear at either of these locations on the return journey. If not, you'll have to take a risk:*

Watch obelisk	go to 83
Watch manor house	go to 39
Don't bother watching here	go to 127

16

It's just a swan! *Delete the top number in your score card's* 📷 *column. Go next to 75.*

17

You peer eagerly out of your compartment window as the eerie road bridge slowly comes closer. You can't see anything at the top of the bridge just yet . . . or can you? Suddenly you think you spot something white moving across it! The trouble is the engine is now puffing under the bridge and the clouds of steam envelop whatever it is up there. But there's definitely something behind that steam; you're absolutely sure of it. You can just make out its vague outline. Perhaps it will be clearer in a photograph . . .

> **If take photo   go to 116**
> **If not   go to 68**

18

As the train starts its return journey, shrieking out of Mistfield station in a cloud of steam, you only hope that the sky won't very soon grow too dark for taking photographs. It's just about light enough at the moment because the rain has eased a little. But the sky will be gradually darkening in the next hour, anyway, so you could really do with the rain easing a lot more! **Go to 56.**

19

You leap into the observation car, grateful to be able to slam the door on all that rain. The rain's not shut out completely, though, because you immediately pull down the window in the door. With the lights now on in the carriage, it's the only way you can see outside! However, it's getting so dark now that there isn't much for you to see out there *anyway*. But, perhaps there will be the odd ghost or two glowing through the darkness! *Go to 29.*

20

Just in case a glowing ghost *might* suddenly appear at one of those shadowy features you can see from the bridge, you decide to point your camera at one of them for a minute or two. But which seems the most promising? That tall observation hut a few hundred metres to the north of the railway line, or that large eerie pond to the south?

If you have circled the M in your score card's  *column, you may study the MAP accessory now to find out if a ghost will appear at either of these locations on the return journey. If not, you'll have to take a risk:*

Watch observation hut	*go to 96*
Watch pond	*go to 60*
Don't bother watching here	*go to 8*

21

The engine's boiler *couldn't* have blown up . . . because you realise with great relief that the train is still moving! Then you notice the fragments of glass on the compartment floor and the missing light above your head. So that's all the explosion was: a faulty light bulb! Your relief is rather spoilt by noticing something else, though – the photograph protruding from the bottom of your camera. Your shock at the explosion must have made you press its shutter-release button!

***Delete the top number in your score card's
column. Go next to 57.***

22

You desperately attempt to keep your viewfinder steady while you try to work out whether this white shape is a ghost . . . or just a blast of steam swirling past the window. Perhaps you could be more certain if you lowered your camera and studied the window with your naked eye. But there isn't time. The ghost – steam – or whatever it might be – is starting to waft away from the glass. A photograph has to be taken either at this very instant or not at all!

If take photo   go to 86
If not   go to 25

It's beginning to look as if there won't be any ghosts appearing along the viaduct on this return journey either. Or certainly not on *this* side of the viaduct. Just as you're thinking this, however, a ghost all but brushes the top of your head, suddenly swooping down towards your open window from above! In your shock you click your camera. Unfortunately, it wasn't pointing in the right direction. Then you see that it wasn't a ghost at all but a swift flitting about after insects. It now seems even more of a wasted photograph!

Delete the top number in your score card's  *column. Go next to 7.*

The train has now travelled a fair number of miles from Littleoak station – with the time approaching eight o'clock. The storm has fortunately stopped at last and, although it's now well into the evening, the sky is still light enough for you to use your camera. And you hope it remains this way for a good hour. That's not to say that it isn't still very eerie-looking outside but at least it's an eeriness that can be captured on film! *Go to 76.*

A few minutes later, jerking and groaning, the train slows down for Mistfield station. As you wait for the platform to appear, you have another quick look at that *Ghost Ride!* brochure you brought with you. It says that the train is expected to return to Bleakwood station a little before ten o'clock. You wonder how many ghosts you will have witnessed by then. And, more importantly, how many you will have caught on film! **Go to 144.**

Well done! You've photographed a ghost! Record this in the 📷 column of your score card. Also, delete the top number in the 🎞 column to deduct the photo used. Go next to 42.

Your watch's slight trembling must simply be because you're on a particularly bumpy section of track at the moment, for there hasn't been so much as a hint of a ghost at the windows so far! You've just put your camera down again when the train suddenly brakes almost to a halt, throwing you into the opposite seat. You poke your head out of the window to see if you can find out the reason for this fierce braking. You see a sheep strolling across the line! Pulling your head back in again, you're met by a far less amusing sight. Your camera has produced a photograph. Its shutter-release button must have been knocked during the jolt!

Delete the top number in your score card's  *column. Go next to 85.*

28

The train's now inside the tunnel, rattling through its eerie darkness. The carriage lights have now finally been switched on – but only for the first few minutes. Then they're suddenly turned off again. The trip's organisers must have ordered this for greater atmosphere! If there had been lots of other passengers in the carriage you might have enjoyed the idea. But not when you're the only one there! The pitch-black tunnel goes on and on, echoing with the engine's eerie, screeching whistles, but at last you see a small patch of light ahead. To your relief, you're finally coming out of the tunnel! *Go next to 152.*

29

You don't spot any ghostly glows *before* you reach Grimley Tunnel, nor when you're actually *in* the tunnel . . . but you're hoping that you'll have a bit more luck now that you're about to emerge from it. You remember seeing a water mill not far from this end of the tunnel, a little to the north of the track. And a large clump of trees about the same distance to the south. Perhaps near one of *these* is where you'll see your ghostly glow!

If you have circled the M in your score card's 📖 *column, you may study the MAP accessory now to find out if a ghost will appear at either of these locations on the return journey. If not, you'll have to take a risk:*

Watch for water mill	go to 97
Watch for trees	go to 38
Don't bother watching here	go to 57

30

As you walk towards the tiny ticket office, you're certainly not expecting to find anyone serving there. It's obvious that this station is now merely a halt. The derelict road leading up to the station – and the tangled greenery all round it – show that the days when people actually boarded here passed long ago! *Go to 119.*

31

Craning your neck a little further out of the compartment window, you notice a white signal just before the viaduct. Is it here that a ghost will suddenly appear? You lift your camera to your eye, framing the signal in its viewfinder. Your finger trembles excitedly on the shutter-release button as the extended signal arm suddenly starts to vibrate a little. Then it suddenly drops and, in shock, you fully depress the button. You immediately feel like kicking yourself, though, realising that you'd over-reacted. It is, of course, perfectly natural for the signal arm to change positions once in a while!

Delete the top number in your score card's  ***column. Go next to 66.***

'Much obliged for your help,' the driver says to you when the four of you have finally managed to drag the tree clear of the line. He and the stoker are much friendlier than Ted and they both give you a grateful slap on the back with their grimy hands. 'Now we'd all better get on board again,' the driver says hurriedly.

'This tree must have put us a good ten minutes behind schedule!' You wonder which part of the train you should quickly haul yourself into . . .

If first class carriage	*go to 107*
If second class carriage	*go to 55*
If observation car	*go to 146*

33

The train is now approaching the little footbridge and you lower the compartment window as far down as it will go so you can look directly upwards with your camera. So much rain blows into the compartment, though, that you suddenly lose your footing on the damp floor. It's bad enough to fall flat on your back – but even worse is that soft whirring noise you hear from your camera. It's producing a photograph!

Delete the top number in your score card's 📷 column. Go next to 85.

34

You move right into the corridor with your camera to ensure you obtain as clear a photograph as possible of the isolated telephone box. It's partly hidden by a tree at the moment but it should soon be unobscured. Yes, you now have a full view of the telephone box . . . and you notice a shadowy figure inside it! *Go to 118.*

35

Still you can't see any daylight ahead of you but you know the tunnel will have to end eventually. And, when it does, you wonder whether there will be any ghosts lurking around. Near the tunnel's exit would perhaps be a perfect place for them! So you consider where you should be pointing your camera as the exit finally approaches – towards its left side or its right? Or shouldn't you bother with either side of the tunnel? Perhaps the ghosts like it in here no more than you do!

If you have circled the N in your score card's ▨▨
column, you may consult the NEWSPAPER access-

ory now to find out if a ghost will appear near the
tunnel's exit. If not, you'll have to take a risk:

Watch its left side	*go to 92*
Watch its right side	*go to 43*
Don't bother watching here	*go to 152*

36

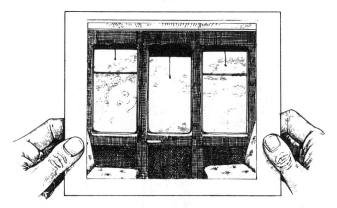

Well risked! Record this success in the 🖼 column of
your score card. Also, delete the top number in the
📷 column to deduct the photo used. Go next to 75.

37

'What was this terrible tragedy exactly?' you ask the
stoker a little apprehensively. To begin with, you
thought he might just be spinning you a great yarn –

another bit of 'atmosphere' for your trip! But the gloom spreading across his face tells you that he is absolutely serious. 'It's what a stoker always fears the most,' he says solemnly. 'An engine's boiler suddenly exploded. It happened at this very station, apparently, just as the train was passing that signal box over there. Sadly, the signalman and both the engine's driver and stoker all came a cropper in the ferocious blast.' ***Go next to 110.***

38
Grimley Tunnel is now some three miles behind you and you reckon it's roughly about here that you spotted that clump of trees on the outward journey. Yes, there it is – because the eerie silhouette is suddenly illuminated by a flash of lightning! Moments later, you think you see a glow coming from that direction. Is it simply your

eyes reacting to the bright flash or is there a ghost amongst the trees? The only way to be sure is to take a photograph in that direction . . .

If take photo *go to 123*
If not *go to 57*

39

There's nothing strange to be seen near the eerie manor house for the moment. And it's then obscured for a while by a long line of overgrown trees right next to the track. There are still occasional glimpses of the house, but they aren't sufficient for you to be able to tell whether a ghost has suddenly appeared there. The line of trees finally peters out – but not before one of the overgrown branches nearly flicks you in the face! You just have time, fortunately, to duck back from the window. But you knock your camera's shutter-release button in the process!

Delete the top number in your score card's 📷 *column. Go next to 127.*

It's merely a tent you photographed: the glow being produced by someone suddenly turning on a lamp inside! *Delete the top number in your score card's*  *column. Go next to 8.*

41

You keep your eye glued to your camera's viewfinder, waiting for the signal box suddenly to appear there as the train creeps towards it. Ah, here it is . . . and isn't that a hazy figure standing inside the box? Could it be the ghost of a signalman from the past? When you lift your eyes from the viewfinder, though, and stare directly at the signal box, you see that the figure in there isn't as hazy as you thought. He's a quite normal, flesh-

and-blood signalman, who's now waving at you through the glass! It's a good job you didn't waste one of your precious photographs on him. ***Go to 144.***

42

You now wander along the carriage's corridor, popping your head into each of the rather dingy compartments. You're still hoping that you'll find some other passengers on board! You don't, of course – and, to be honest, it would probably have unnerved you more if you suddenly *had* found someone. There's been absolutely nowhere they could have got on! ***Go to 164.***

43

You feel your way out of the dark compartment, knowing that you'll obtain a much better view of the right side of the tunnel exit from the corridor. Barely have you pulled down one of the windows there than the tunnel exit at last appears ahead. You can just make out a pin-prick of light. But as that pin-prick quickly grows bigger, you think you can see something just in front of it as well. It's something white . . . and it's hovering! You hope to wait until whatever it is becomes a little clearer before deciding whether to take a photograph – but the approach of the train makes the thing suddenly start to fly off. So you must make that decision right now!

If take photo   go to 72
If not   go to 152

44

Well done! You've caught a ghost on film! Record this in the 👻 *column of your score card. Also delete the top number in the* 📷 *column to deduct the photo used. Go next to 28.*

No sooner have you sat down in one of the first class compartments than the train reaches Dark Valley. It starts to cross a huge viaduct that spans the valley. You're peering right down into the gloomy valley when you think you hear a gentle tapping sound. It seems to be coming from behind you – from one of the windows in the corridor. You don't see anything when you turn round, but you wonder if this tapping is a warning that a ghost is about to appear at a corridor window! You glance at your watch. It's coming up to five past eight. Is this a time particularly favoured by the ghosts?

If you have circled the T in your score card's 📖 *column, you may consult the TIMETABLE accessory now to find out if a ghost will appear at this carriage at this time. If not, you'll have to take a risk:*
    Watch corridor windows   *go to 142*
    Don't bother watching   *go to 75*

Walking up to the luggage trolley, you start to look at the labels on the leather trunks. They're all very old and scarcely legible. You then can't resist trying the catches on some of the trunks so you can see what's inside. Just as you'd rather expected, though, every single one is locked. You now start walking towards the other end of the platform so you can examine the weighing-machine. You're about halfway there, however, when you suddenly slip on a small patch of oil. Fortunately, you're not too close to the edge of the platform, but you do press your camera's shutter-release button as you stumble and waste one of those precious remaining photographs!

Delete the top number in your score card's 📷 column. Go next to 69.

The faint camera at one of the windows shows that it was just a reflection of your own face after all! How could you have been so stupid as to have wasted yet another precious photograph? **Delete the top number in your score card's 📷 column. Go next to 24.**

You quickly open your compartment door so you can watch the corridor windows as well. Raising your camera to your eye, you keep looking from one side to the other; first inside your compartment, then outside. You've just turned to the corridor windows a third time when something large and white suddenly appears, flapping outside one of them! It looks as if it's about to leave again immediately – so you must decide about a photograph this very instant!

> **If take photo** **go to 94**
> **If not** **go to 24**

You keep your eyes firmly fixed on the castle as the train rumbles across the viaduct. But if a ghost *does* sometimes haunt the ruin, it certainly doesn't look as if it's going to make an appearance for *you*! Perhaps you would have done better to watch the stone bridge instead. Hoping it's not too late, you hurriedly cross to the other side of the observation car. You're in a bit too much of a hurry, though, because you suddenly trip. Fortunately, you and your camera land in one of the seats. But you must have knocked the camera's shutter-release button as you tumbled, for a photograph is starting to come out of your camera!

Delete the top number in your score card's  *column. Go next to 75.*

50

Having taken a seat in the observation car, you watch the rain slide down its broad windows while you wait for the train to leave the station. Finally the carriage gives a sudden jolt and then starts to clank forward. As it creeps along beside the platform, you wonder whether any ghosts will appear on your way out of the station. Perhaps one will be looking down at you as you pass under that footbridge . . . or one will be staring out from that signal box. Or perhaps one will be hovering above that rusty water tank that you'd noticed just beyond the platform!

If you have circled the N in your score card's  column, you may consult the NEWSPAPER accessory now to find out if a ghost is likely to appear as the train leaves Littleoak station. If not, you'll have to take a risk:

Watch footbridge	*go to 136*
Watch signal box	*go to 5*
Watch water tank	*go to 70*
Don't bother watching here	*go to 24*

51

After Ted has disappeared down the corridor again, you peer out of your compartment window to see if you can spot Mistfield station yet. Is that it in the murky distance? It might be, it might not – but what suddenly attracts your interest even more for the moment is a rather spooky-looking manor house a few hundred metres to the left of the railway line . . . *Go to 100.*

You can't help trembling a little as you point your camera straight downwards from the viaduct. The bottom of the valley is now almost completely dark, the river quite undetectable. Suddenly, however, you think you spot a glow moving in that darkness. Could it be a ghost? You're being far too hopeful, though, because the straight line in which the glow is moving – and its snail-like speed – suggest that it's surely just a boat travelling along the river. Anyway, you can at least now feel satisfied that you've had a thorough look at the spooky valley . . . and finally raise your eyes from it. *Go to 7.*

When you try the door to the tea room, though, you find that it is firmly locked. Peering in at the dark window, you are just able to make out a couple of wooden tables inside and, at the far end, a little counter bearing a metal tea urn. You now turn away from the window but then you suddenly swing your head back to it. You're sure you saw the lid of that urn lifting a little and steam rising out of it! The urn certainly looks perfectly innocent now, though. The eerie atmosphere of the place is obviously making your eyes play tricks on you! *Go to 148.*

54

'We'll be coming to Grimley Tunnel first,' Ted tells you as the train now starts to accelerate a little. 'I think I'm meant to make funny noises in there so the passengers will think it's full of ghosts,' he adds grumpily. 'But since you're the only one, I won't bother if it's all the same to you. I've got much better things to do with my time – like polishing the mirrors and brushing down the seats. Anyway, if you need me I'll be in the first class carriage, right at the front. You might as well feel free to wander into any carriage you want since you're the only passenger. You can either remain 'ere in the observation car, go through to the second class carriage, or join me in the first.'

Which will you choose?
If observation car	**go to 11**
If second class carriage	**go to 147**
If first class carriage	**go to 78**

55
You step into one of the compartments in the second class carriage but then you suddenly pause. *Was it* the storm that had brought down that tree – or was it something more sinister than that? Perhaps a ghost had pushed it on to the line! And maybe it had done so as some sort of warning, to let it be known that it was about to make an appearance at one of the train's windows! You therefore step back into the corridor so you have a

view of as many windows as possible. You also check your watch; it's coming up to eight-twenty. You wonder if this is a good time for a ghost's appearance.

If you have circled the T in your score card's 📚 column, you may consult the TIMETABLE accessory now to find out if a ghost will appear at this carriage at this time. If not, you'll have to take a risk:

    Watch carriage windows   *go to 4*
    Don't bother watching yet   *go to 154*

56

Despite your worries about it, the light still just about holds until you reach that road bridge again – and even until you're approaching that spooky viaduct some ten minutes later. You peer southwards as you start crossing the viaduct, down towards that dilapidated boathouse on the near bank of the river and then that ruined castle on the far bank. Should you expect ghosts at either of these places?

If you have circled the M in your score card's 📚 column, you may study the MAP accessory now to find out if a ghost will appear at either of these locations on the return journey. If not, you'll have to take a risk:

    Watch boathouse   *go to 102*
    Watch castle   *go to 74*
    Don't bother watching here   *go to 9*

57

Your eerie excursion is finally about to end because the
train is now pulling into Bleakwood station. As you step
down from your carriage you look along the shadowy
platform for Ted in order to thank him. However, it
takes him quite a while to leave the train and start
shuffling towards you and when he does you notice how
pale his face is. In fact, it's completely white! 'I take
back all that I said about them ghosts,' his voice
trembles in barely a whisper. 'During that last part of
the journey, I *did* see one. The railway line's definitely
h-haunted, I swear it.' Ted can swear it all he likes,
though. The only way people are going to *believe* that
the Dark Valley railway line is haunted is if you can
produce photographic evidence!

So what's the final score in your 💀 *column? If it's at*
least one, then you do have this photographic evi-
dence. But the evidence will only be absolutely

convincing (**convincing enough to win your school newspaper that award!**) if you have the maximum score of SIX ghost photographs. So if your  score is any less than six, try playing the game again to see if you can improve on it!

58

You slowly open your eyes and are able to tell from the different sound the train is making that the viaduct is behind you at last. You should now very soon be coming up to Littleoak station again. Here you really *must* keep your eyes open for ghosts. You might not have many chances left! You wonder if you're likely to have more luck watching the signal box as the train chugs into the station – or that little footbridge?

If you have circled the N in your score card's column, *you may consult the NEWSPAPER accessory now to find out where a ghost will appear as the train approaches Littleoak station on the return journey. If not, you'll have to take a risk:*

Watch signal box	go to 103
Watch footbridge	go to 33
Don't bother watching here	go to 85

Your watch shows that there are only *five* seconds to go now until half past eight and you quickly point your camera at the compartment window. You feel it start to tremble a little in your hands as the last couple of seconds tick by. Then, exactly on cue, a floating white shape appears at the window! *Go to 22.*

60

You're just about to snap the eerie pond, having noticed a dark figure moving around behind it! But then you realise that it's just a supple tree blowing about in the wind. A few seconds later, though, you can make out something else which could be a ghost. There's a strange glow amongst those dark reeds waving about at the edge of the pond! You're convinced that the glow is gradually moving through the reeds but you daren't watch it for too long in case it suddenly disappears. If you're going to take a photograph, it really ought to be right now!

If take photo   go to 77
If not   go to 8

Hard luck. It *was* just steam you were looking at!
Delete the top number in your score card's 📷
column. Go next to 152.

'How are you getting on with the ghosts?' the stoker
asks you with a chuckle, nodding at your camera. 'I'd
have no chance seeing them myself, of course, because I
have to spend the whole journey shovelling coal into the
boiler. Barely have time to look up, I don't! But I'm not
quite as sceptical about them as ol' Ted. It's not just
what that Walter Potts said. I've been reading up about
this line and apparently there was a terrible tragedy here
in the last century. Well, as you know, where there are
tragedies, they say you often get ghosts!' ***Go to 37.***

63

You realise that this sudden darkness must be because the train has just entered the Grimley Tunnel that Ted had mentioned. You wonder why the carriage lights don't go on but you suppose they've been left off *deliberately* for greater atmosphere! And atmosphere there certainly is in this long tunnel for, jerking down your compartment window, you can't see even the faintest glimmer of light ahead. There's just the occasional eerie scream echoing back at you from the engine's whistle. At least, you hope it's from the engine's whistle! *Go to 35.*

You crouch down on the carriage floor, pointing your camera as high up as you can. If there *is* anything floating around above the tunnel entrance, you should just be able to catch it! The hollow screech of the engine's whistle tells you that the front part of the train is now entering the tunnel and you press your camera's viewfinder right against your eye in readiness. All you can see above the tunnel's brick entrance, though, are thick clouds of steam. You're sure there's no ghost amongst them. So you get up from your crouching position but, as you do so, the train suddenly jolts you forward. You've knocked your camera's shutter-release button!

Delete the top number in your score card's 📷 *column. Go next to 28.*

65

You keep the cottage carefully centred in your camera's viewfinder as it gradually moves towards the edge of the train's wide window. It's just about to pass out of sight altogether when you notice a dark figure some way in front of it. Maybe this is just a farmer strolling across the fields – but surely a farmer wouldn't be strolling on an evening as wretched as this? And why are his arms so strangely outstretched as he walks? In fact, is he walking at all? The eerie figure just seems to be standing there, mysteriously watching the train as it passes. You're becoming more and more convinced that this is a ghost and you wonder if a photograph would confirm it. The photograph would have to be taken immediately, though!

If take photo go to 10
If not go to 105

66

You're now most of the way across the scary viaduct and you're ready to take a breath at last. You've been holding it for the last few minutes! Just at that moment, though, the train comes to a halt. You pray that it hasn't broken down – for there's still a good thirty-metre drop beneath you. What if you had to walk the rest of the way to the end of the viaduct, balancing on that thin wall? Fortunately, however, the train at last starts to move again. *Now*, perhaps, you can take that breath! **Go to 75.**

67

You leap into the second class carriage, keen to be out of that drenching rain. It's not long afterwards that the train starts to leave the storm-swept station, making its way towards Grimley Tunnel again. You wonder if you'll see something hovering at the windows during this last part of the journey. You don't have any luck before you reach Grimley Tunnel – nor actually *inside* it – but, on emerging from the tunnel, you check your watch. The time is coming up to nine-forty. Perhaps this is when a ghost will make its appearance!

If you have circled the T in your score card's 🚂 *column, you may consult the TIMETABLE accessory now to find out if a ghost will appear at this carriage at this time. If not, you'll have to take a risk:*

   Watch windows   **go to 95**
   Don't bother watching here   **go to 57**

68

A few minutes after you have passed under the road bridge, you hear an eerie shuffling sound coming towards you from a little further up the corridor. Perhaps there was a ghost haunting the bridge after all and it actually boarded the train! You nervously jam your foot against the closed compartment door as the shuffling comes nearer. Should you quickly draw down the blinds as well . . . or wouldn't that make any difference? Perhaps ghosts can see through blinds . . . and, come to think of it, they can most certainly pass through jammed doors! *Go next to 143.*

69

A loud screech is emitted from the engine shed and the steam train finally emerges. Its black silhouette slowly becomes visible through the billowing clouds of steam. You make your way quickly back up the footbridge, disappearing for a moment in some of this steam as the train and its three carriages rattle noisily underneath.

'Passengers for the *Ghost Ride*?' a rather surly guard asks as he holds the carriage door open for you. He wears little round glasses and has rather drooping shoulders. 'You're the only one, are you?' he mutters. 'Suppose everyone else saw it for the silly nonsense it was. Ghost Ride indeed! I thought the purpose of them renovating this line was to bring back the good old days of steam – not to exploit it with daft gimmicks!' *Go next to 160.*

70

You cross to the best window for the water tank as the train jerks you nearer and nearer to it. You can now just about see the tank beside the track and you quickly lift your camera up to your eye. The viewfinder shows nothing out of the ordinary about it, however. You certainly can't see any ghosts hovering around near it! Disappointed, you're just lowering your camera again when the train gives another of its sudden jolts and throws you forward. Fortunately, you manage to keep hold of your camera as you fall to the floor, but, infuriatingly, you can't help squeezing the shutter-release button!

Delete the top number in your score card's 📷 column. Go next to 24.

71

You poke your head even further out of the window, pointing your camera up at the approaching footbridge. You can't see anything hovering there at the moment. But then you can't even see the *bridge*, let alone a ghost! For the bridge is suddenly enveloped in clouds of white steam as the engine now starts to pass underneath it. These clouds gradually disperse as your carriage rumbles slowly forward, though, and you can now just make out a shadowy figure through the steam. Is this the ghost you were hoping for – or just a station official standing on the footbridge? You'll have to make up your mind quickly because you'll be reaching the bridge yourself any moment and by the time you've passed underneath the figure might have disappeared!

> **If take photo**   *go to 111*
> **If not**   *go to 144*

72

It was just an owl in the tunnel – and a waste of a photograph, unfortunately! ***Delete the top number in your score card's 📷 column. Go next to 152.***

Wandering into the waiting-room, you have a quick look at all the old advertisements on the walls. Some are for confectionery, some for rail holidays to the seaside, and some even for strange things like shoe polish! The prices displayed are all old-fashioned ones like 5/4d or 3d. You're just wondering how much 5/4d would be worth in modern currency when the door suddenly slams shut behind you. Was it the wind that caused this – or was it something rather more sinister? Just in case it was the latter, you quickly leave the rather eerie room! *Go next to 104.*

74

Just for a moment, you think you *do* spot a ghost hovering above the castle. You quickly bring your camera to your eye but then you realise that it's just a large flag fluttering at the top of the ruin. You're chuckling at your mistake when the train suddenly squeals to an abrupt halt, throwing you violently to the floor. Before you have time to pick yourself up again, Ted comes panting into your carriage. He wants to know why you pulled the communication cord! *Go to 129.*

75

Having finally reached the other side of the viaduct, the train then works up to a much faster speed again. It's now travelling at some thirty-five miles per hour. After a while, though, it grinds to a sudden halt, throwing you to the carriage floor. It's fortunate that your camera was sitting at your feet or you could well have smashed it – or, at the very least, knocked its shutter-release button! But you *have* knocked your elbow and you give it a rub before lowering the window to see if you can discover the cause of the sudden stop. *Go to 2.*

76

You're beginning to make out a deep valley some distance ahead, cutting right across the path of the railway line. This, you assume, is *Dark* Valley – from where the railway obtained its name. You decide to seek out Ted to verify this and so you start to make your way along the jerking train. *Go to 159.*

Unfortunately, it was just a night-time fisherman! And, sadly, you've wasted another precious photograph. *Delete the top number in your score card's* 📷 *column. Go next to 8.*

78

You follow Ted towards the first class carriage, squeezing through the rather dingy second class carriage on the way. The first class carriage is a little smarter but even this one has obviously seen better days! The carriage isn't open-plan like modern ones but divided into separate, rather cramped, compartments. 'If you need me for any reason,' Ted grunts as he leaves you in the jerking corridor, 'I'll be brushing down the compartment right at the front. But don't bother calling me if it's just to say that you've seen a ghost. 'Cos I won't believe you!' *Go to 126.*

79

Under this lighter sky you can now just make out what looks like a ruined abbey approaching to your left, halfway to the horizon. Turning your head away from the window and peering into the corridor, you see that a stone building is approaching to the right as well. This one is rather nearer to the railway line, though, and you're sure it's some sort of farmhouse. You wonder whether you should keep your eyes on one of these two buildings in case a ghost suddenly appears there!

If you have circled the M in your score card's 🖦 *column, you may study the MAP accessory now to find out if a ghost will appear at either of these two locations. If not, you'll have to take a risk:*

Watch abbey	go to 106
Watch farmhouse	go to 163
Don't bother watching here	go to 24

Eagerly unfolding the small sheet of paper, you find that it's a coloured sketch-map of the railway line. And a fairly old sketch by the look of it. Judging by how faded it is, you would guess that the map has lain hidden behind that chocolate machine ever since the line operated a proper railway service all those years ago! Examining the sketch more closely, you become absolutely sure of this. Little 'ghost' symbols have been painted in at various locations on the map and printed across the top of the map are the words *Ghost appearances some distance from railway line*. It was obviously the handiwork of Walter Potts, the guard who claimed that the railway line was haunted!

You are now entitled to use the MAP accessory. Circle the M in the  *column of your score card so that you have a reminder of this whenever the map is required. Go next to 148.*

The clouds of steam at last start to lift from the water tank, its faint silhouette becoming clearer and clearer behind them. You're sure there's the silhouette of a person there as well. No, it must be a ghost – because the hazy figure is near the top of the water tank, a good five or six metres off the ground! As the steam rapidly lifts further, though, you see that it's just the train's stoker. He must have jumped down from the engine as it was creeping towards the station so he could check the water tank. And the reason he's several metres in the air is that he's standing on a ladder attached to the tall container! *Go to 144.*

You move your camera until the eerie-looking manor house is right in the centre of its viewfinder. You're now all set to take a photograph, should a ghost suddenly appear there. And one *does* suddenly appear, snaking up from the house's shadowy chimney-pots! No, it's just wisps of smoke. You realise this just a fraction too late, though, because in your excitement you've already pressed the camera's shutter-release button!

Delete the top number in your score card's 📷 column. Go next to 25.

83

You have to hold your camera quite a way out of the compartment window to capture the obelisk in its viewfinder. You then gasp with excitement. What's that strange white mist that's suddenly appeared to one side of the obelisk? Could it actually be a ghost? Perhaps the mist is just condensation on your lens, though. What you really need to do is lower your camera so you can study the obelisk for a moment with your naked eye. But you don't *have* this moment, for the obelisk will have completely disappeared in the next second!

If take photo   **go to 145**
If not   **go to 127**

84

You poke your head as far out of the window as you dare as the viaduct approaches and peer down at the tall, dark arches which support it. You hope they're sound! They're certainly very sinister-looking in this gloomy light. So you lift your camera to your eye, ready for any ghosts that might suddenly float up from the arches. But as the train now actually starts to cross the viaduct, the long drop you can see through your viewfinder makes you feel giddier and giddier. And, in steadying yourself, you accidentally press your camera's shutter-release button!

Delete the top number in your score card's 📷 *column. Go next to 66.*

85

'Littleoak station . . . welcome to Littleoak station!' a whispery voice announces from one of its platforms as the train now shudders towards them. At least, you *thought* that's where the voice came from but when you step down from the train you see that the station is just as deserted as it was before. The voice must have been Ted's, calling out from one of the carriage windows . . . *Go to 135.*

86

Definitely a ghost – well done! Record this success in the ☻ *column of your score card. Also, delete the top number in the* 📷 *column to deduct the photo used. Go next to 25.*

You poke your head right out of this window, the rain driving furiously into your eyes. It really stings but you try to ignore it, keeping your camera trained on the embankment just ahead of you. Suddenly, you think you see a momentary glow of a ghost there – but there's a rumble of thunder a few seconds later and you wonder whether that glow was just a lightning flash reflected through the camera. The white glow momentarily appears again, though, and this time there isn't any thunder to follow! Not for quite a while, anyway. Perhaps the very next time you glimpse that glow, you should immediately press the shutter-release button . . .

If take photo   *go to 158*
If not   *go to 57*

You shake the droplets of rain off as soon as you have climbed into the first class carriage. You then flop down in one of its compartments. All you can do now is wait until the train brings you back to Bleakwood station. Now that the lights have been switched on in the carriages, attempting to see anything outside – even anything right next to the track – will be impossible. It's only when you've passed through Grimley Tunnel again and are nearly back at Bleakwood station that you realise how stupid you've been. Of course, all you had to do was open the windows to be able to see outside! *Go to 109.*

89

You anxiously study the sky from your first class compartment as the train begins its return journey. Although the rain isn't quite as heavy as it was, the remaining light will surely be fading fairly soon anyway. The light just manages to hold, though, until you're back at that road bridge – and even until the train approaches that long viaduct which spans Dark Valley. *Go to 155.*

90

Your camera all checked, you start to wonder whether there *might* just be something ghost-like along the railway line. Perhaps there will be something as you enter the *Grimley Tunnel* that Ted mentioned! So you consider where you should point your camera as the tunnel entrance approaches – at its left side, at its right side, or directly above it? But maybe there won't be a ghost *anywhere* at the tunnel entrance. Perhaps you should just put your camera down for the time being and wait until you're further along the railway line . . .

If you have circled the **N** *in your score card's* 📰 *column, you may consult the NEWSPAPER accessory now to find out if a ghost is likely to appear at the tunnel entrance on the outward journey. If not, you'll have to take a risk:*

Watch its left side	*go to 131*
Watch its right side	*go to 157*
Watch above it	*go to 64*
Don't bother watching here	*go to 28*

No, there isn't a ghost. There's nothing but clouds of steam! *Delete the top number in your score card's  column. Go next to 24.*

92

Careful not to lean out too far, you hold your camera up to your eye at the opened window. You can at last glimpse the end of the tunnel ahead and you place your finger on the camera's shutter-release button in readiness. Your finger suddenly starts to tremble in your excitement. Is that a ghost hovering just in front of the growing circle of light at the exit – or is it just a cloud of steam from the engine? But then you think you see a pair of red eyes amongst the whitish vapours. Or is there a rational explanation for that too? Perhaps they're just glowing specks of coal emitted from the engine's funnel. You're really not sure whether you should quickly take a photograph or not!

If take photo   go to 61
If not   go to 152

93

A moment later, though, you notice a couple of rabbits scampering out from underneath the bushes. So that's all the rustling was. You're just removing the camera from your face when suddenly you feel something brush the back of your neck! You snap a photograph in shock. But this wasn't anything to do with ghosts either. It was just your camera strap rubbing against your neck!

Delete the top number in your score card's 📷 *column. Go next to 68.*

You were mistaken. It was just a sheet of newspaper that the storm had blown against the window! *Delete the top number in your score card's*  *column. Go next to 24.*

A shrill scream from the engine's whistle suddenly rends the silence outside. Or was it from the engine's whistle? Perhaps it was a ghost making that spine-chilling sound! In case it was, you quickly move your camera round the carriage windows. As you're doing this, you suddenly hear a loud explosion. Has there been a terrible accident? Has the engine's boiler blown up, just like that one did all those years ago? *Go to 21.*

As you point your camera at the rapidly-darkening observation hut, you wonder *what* exactly is observed from there. The fact that the hut is on tall stilts makes you think it must be birds–and you've certainly noticed a good variety of birds in this remote countryside over the last couple of hours; everything from wild ducks and geese to hawks and owls! But you suddenly don't care what the hut is used for. A strange glow has appeared just beneath it . . . in the vague shape of a ghost! Worried that the glow might vanish as quickly as it has come, you tell yourself that if you're going to take a photograph, it must be right now!

If take photo   *go to 40*
If not   *go to 8*

Having now emerged from the tunnel, you try to calculate roughly where it would be that you noticed the water mill on the outward journey. Was it about two miles from the tunnel . . . or three? You're saved having to work this out, though, because the water mill is suddenly lit up in a long flash of violet lightning. You aim your camera at this spot as soon as the lightning has gone, and try to keep it aimed there for a good couple of minutes. But the water mill must be well behind you by now – and, disappointingly, you saw no strange glows from that vicinity! *Go to 57.*

98

You step into the nearest compartment through its sliding door and pull the window right down to give yourself as clear a view as possible of the water mill. All the rain outside has made the glass steam up a little. As you squint at the mill. you think you *do* suddenly see something there. There's something white and vapoury hovering at the side of the huge water wheel! But then you wonder if this is just the spray that the wheel is throwing out as it rotates. It's so hard to tell from this distance. Perhaps whatever it is would be clearer on a photograph where everything is frozen. If you *are* going to use your camera, though, you must do it right now before you have passed the water mill.

If take photo *go to 26*
If not *go to 42*

99

'We'll be coming into Littleoak station soon,' Ted grunts when you've found him. He's checking that the bulbs are all secure in one of the first class compartments. 'The train stops there for nearly ten minutes if you want to stretch yer legs,' he adds in another grunt. Yes, your legs *could* do with a stretch – and so a short while later you step down on to the desolate station. Since there isn't time to explore all of it, you decide to concentrate on just one area. The question is – which?

If ticket office *go to 30*
If waiting-room *go to 73*
If signal box *go to 128*

This spooky-looking manor house would surely be the perfect place for a ghost's appearance and you wonder whether you should point your camera at its distant silhouette. But, turning your head towards the corridor window this time, you can just make out an old telephone box. This too is quite a distance from the line and is, strangely, right in the middle of nowhere. You could quite imagine a ghost suddenly appearing there as well! So the only question is, which direction do you point your camera?

If you have circled the M in your score card's 🦇 *column, you may study the MAP accessory now to find out if a ghost will appear at either of these locations on the outward journey. If not, you'll have to take a risk:*

Watch manor house	*go to 82*
Watch telephone box	*go to 34*
Don't bother watching here	*go to 25*

You just make the observation car in time because the train is now puffing on to the viaduct which spans Dark Valley. You peer down at the hazy river far below, which makes you feel quite giddy. You sincerely hope that this viaduct has been checked for any cracks that might have developed over the years! Your eye now wanders some distance up the river – towards where a shadowy stone bridge crosses it. Peering about the same distance *down* the river, you spot a ruined castle on its near bank. Stone bridge? Castle? Which of these two is more likely to have a ghost suddenly appearing there?

*If you have circled the M in your score card's
column, you may study the MAP accessory now to find out if a ghost will appear at either of these locations on the outward journey. If not, you'll have to take a risk:*

Watch stone bridge	**go to 161**
Watch castle	**go to 49**
Don't bother watching here	**go to 75**

102

You keep your camera aimed at the eerie boathouse, wondering if a ghost might appear on that little jetty in front of it. The train has nearly reached the other side of the viaduct now, though, and still you haven't seen any glowing figures moving about down there. Disappointed, you're just about to lower your camera when you are hurled violently to the carriage floor. For one dreadful moment, you think the train has shot off the viaduct and is plunging into the valley! But then Ted suddenly appears in your carriage, demanding to know why you pulled the communication cord . . . *Go to 129.*

103

You hold your camera just out of the compartment window, all ready for the signal box to pass by. This seems to be it approaching now and you rest your hands firmly on the top of the window to keep the camera very steady. The brass strip here has become so wet from the constant rain, however, that your wrists suddenly slip straight off it. You let out a long groan on hearing a soft, whirring noise from your camera. It's the sound of a photograph coming out of it. You obviously pushed the camera's shutter-release button!

Delete the top number in your score card's  ***column. Go next to 85.***

104

Not wishing to be left on this desolate station, you make your way back to the train. There's still a good few minutes to go before it's due to leave . . . but you're not taking any chances! In fact you won't even decide where you want to sit yet. You just tug at the nearest door handle, leaving that decision for when you're actually on the train. Now that you *are* safely on it, though, you consider which carriage you'd like for the next part of the journey.

First class carriage	***go to 165***
Second class carriage	***go to 3***
Observation car	***go to 50***

Soon after the cottage and manor house have disappeared from view, Ted shuffles into your carriage. You wonder if he's come to thank you for helping to move that tree – but no, that would be much too much to hope for! Well, you do receive a bit of a grunt about the tree but the main reason he's come is to tell you that the train will soon be reaching the end of its outward journey. 'We'll be pulling into Mistfield station in just over five minutes,' he mutters. 'Then, when the engine 'as been turned round, it's all the way back again to Bleakwood!' *Go to 150.*

You pull the compartment window up a couple of notches so you can rest your arms on it as you look through your camera at the abbey. This will keep the camera nice and steady. It would break your heart if you caught a ghost on camera only to find that the photo was so blurred no one believed you! It looks as if a ghost *isn't*

going to appear at the abbey, though. The ruin is disappearing behind you now. And, just as it does, the window suddenly gives way under your wrists and slides down to the next notch. You were very lucky that you didn't let go of your camera. But you couldn't help pressing its shutter-release button!

Delete the top number in your score card's  *column. Go next to 24.*

107

You sit down in the first class carriage, waiting for the train to start chugging forward again. The moment it does start to move, though, you intend to be up on your feet. While you were shifting that tree, you could just make out a road bridge several hundred metres further up the line. It was a rather spooky-looking bridge, with dark bushes growing on either side of it, and you wouldn't be surprised if it was haunted! The train *does* now start to clank forward – and you consider which part of the road bridge you should be ready to watch.

If you have circled the N in your score card's  column, you may consult the NEWSPAPER accessory now to find out if a ghost will appear at the road bridge on the outward journey. If not, you'll have to take a risk:

Watch its left side	*go to 156*
Watch its right side	*go to 124*
Watch its top	*go to 17*
Don't bother watching it	*go to 68*

108

You walk up to the old weighing-machine and step on to its rusty platform to see if it still works. It doesn't – the hand on the clock-like face in front of you remains absolutely stationary at the zero mark. Then you notice that you have to insert a coin into the top of the machine. You fish out some coins from your pocket, trying each of them in the slot, but none of them will fit. Of course, a machine as old as this would only take pre-decimal coins! As you step off the machine you suddenly drop the coin you're holding. It rolls right underneath the scales. Crouching down to see if you can reach it, you notice that your coin is not the only thing under there . . . *Go to 133.*

109

Dreading to think how many ghosts you might have stupidly missed during the last twenty minutes or so, you pull down a window right away and stare outside. You hope there'll be just one *more* opportunity to photograph a ghost before the train reaches Bleakwood station. You're sure you will be approaching Bleakwood station at any moment now, though, and so you must instantly decide which *side* of the line you're going to watch for this ghost. Do you watch this right side – or do you quickly lower a window in the corridor and watch its left side?

If you have circled the N in your score card's 👻 *column, you may consult the NEWSPAPER accessory now to find out if a ghost will appear as the train*

near Bleakwood station on its return journey. If not,
you'll have to take a risk:

Watch left side	go to 121
Watch right side	go to 87
Don't bother watching here	go to 57

110

You keep glancing towards the engine, watching the
turntable continuing to move it slowly round. After that
eerie story the stoker told you about this station, you're
anxious to leave it as quickly as possible! At last the
engine has been turned round and it moves off the
turntable, hissing along a short bypass line towards
the observation car which had been at the back of the
train. So this will now be the *front* carriage on the return
journey; followed by the second class, then the first
class carriages. Which of these carriages will you choose
for the next part of your journey?

If observation car	go to 18
If second class carriage	go to 153
If first class carriage	go to 89

Well done! Dressed in very dated clothes like these, this has to be a ghost! And, by the look of it, the ghost of a Victorian station official. Record this success in the 📷 *column of your score card. Also, delete the top number in the* 📷 *column to deduct the photo used. Go next to 144.*

112

You eagerly turn towards the compartment windows in the hope that there *will* be a ghost appearing just before the train finally pulls into Mistfield station. There's certainly nothing at those windows at the moment – but perhaps the ghosts like their appearances to be dramatic and are waiting for the time to reach exactly half past eight! Your watch shows that that's only twenty seconds away now . . .

If you have circled the T in your score card's  *column, you may consult the TIMETABLE accessory now to find out if a ghost will appear at this first class carriage at this time. If not, you'll have to take a risk:*

Watch compartment windows	**go to 59**
Don't bother watching	**go to 25**

113

You decide to while away these five minutes by walking to the station's little footbridge. Climbing up the wooden steps, you survey the state of the sky in the distance. That last trace of light has now gone for good, the darkness rapidly consuming one silhouette after another. So no more chances for any photographs! But there are one or two features still just about visible, those not too far from the railway line. And, although these features themselves might not come out on a photograph, any ghost hovering there might . . . as long as the ghost gives out a strong glow, that is! *Go to 20.*

114

As soon as you've pulled yourself up again, you examine that strange white powder yourself and rub some of it between your fingers. It's as cold as ice! Like Ted, you start nervously to wonder about this . . . but not for very long, for you suddenly notice your camera as it dangles from your neck. It's produced a photograph. You must have knocked the shutter-release button when you were thrown to the floor!

Delete the top number in your score card's  *column. Go next to 9.*

115

You quickly step out into the corridor and pull down a window there as well. There are quite a lot of trees on this right side of the line just before the viaduct. You look from one to the next, wondering if there will soon be a ghost floating near any of them. Your gaze is suddenly fixed on the dense foliage of a huge oak tree.

What's causing its branches to rustle so much? Is it just the wind or is there something about to jump out of them? Some of the leafy branches suddenly start to separate and you hurriedly lift your camera up to your eye as something light-coloured springs out of the hole that is opening up. Should you immediately take a photograph or not?

*If take photo** **go to 149*
*If not** **go to 66*

116

It was just a cow sauntering across the bridge! **Delete the top number in your score card's 📷 column. Go next to 68.**

117

You have only a very quick look at the water tank. This part of the platform at the very end isn't covered by the wooden canopy and you've already been drenched enough as it is! You've just turned away from the huge, rusty tank when you hear its hose arm suddenly creak round in the wind, almost as if it's following you. At least, you *thought* you heard it swing round. But when you turn back again to look, you see that the hose is in exactly the same position as it was before. It must have been that little station sign suspended above you that made the eerie creaking sound. If it wasn't, then either your ears were playing tricks on you . . . or there's something very sinister indeed about that water tank!
Go next to 148.

118

Unable to work out where the figure could have come from, you excitedly press your camera's shutter-release button, convinced that it's a ghost. But as the puffing train presents you with an even better view of the telephone box, you see that there isn't a dark figure inside it at all. It was just a shadowy bush directly behind the glass box. You can't wait for this impulsively-taken photograph to develop . . . just so you can angrily tear it up!

Delete the top number in your score card's 📷 *column. Go next to 25.*

119

Stepping inside the deserted ticket office, you walk up to the little window where the tickets were actually sold. You pull away the cobwebs from this window and peer through the cracked glass. You then crouch down at the little open fireplace nearby, examining the empty grate. The grate clearly hasn't been used for years – even though there's a full coal scuttle standing right next to it. This is just another curio purely for appearances' sake! You suddenly over-balance as you're crouching and knock the scuttle over. You notice a small notebook amongst the scattered coal . . . *Go to 162.*

120

Barely have you poked your camera out of a corridor window than you think you see something on the left wall of the viaduct! Isn't that a hazy figure some distance ahead, balancing on the low wall? You squint even harder through your camera's viewfinder, wanting to be absolutely sure it is a figure. But perhaps it's just a splash of rain on your lens. You're just about to turn your camera round to check, however, when the 'figure' seems to move. So you don't have time for examining your lens. The photograph must be taken right now!

If take photo   **go to 134**
If not   **go to 7**

121
Starting to peer out of one of the corridor windows, you straightaway think you see a ghost near the track! You're frantically lifting your camera to your face, though, when you realise that it's just your eyes playing tricks on you. They had been confused by those bouncing reflections of light from the carriages ahead of you! *Go to 57.*

Did you say that it was a relief to discover that there was a thunderstorm outside? Well, you're beginning to change your mind! The storm grows fiercer and fiercer, making the bleak countryside more and more menacing. It becomes full of rainy shadows and eerie silhouettes. Since it's far too dark to use your camera until the storm eases a little, you decide to go and have another chat with Ted. You know how grumpy he is but when the scenery is as unfriendly as this even Ted's company is better than none at all! *Go to 99.*

Well risked! Record this success in the  *column of your score card. Also, delete the top number in the* *column to deduct the photo used. Go next to 57.*

You slide open your compartment door and step out into the corridor, ready for the approach of the road bridge. You can now just glimpse its steep right bank – and the dense, eerie foliage that climbs up it. Your finger grows more and more tense on your camera's shutter-release button as that bank comes closer. Will a ghost suddenly appear above the dense bushes . . . or a grinning skeleton rise up from the undergrowth? You still can't spot anything there but a sudden bang behind you makes you press the button anyway. What a waste of a precious photograph. It was just the compartment door sliding shut!

Delete the top number in your score card's  ***column. Go next to 68.***

You're sure Ted's right about this trip being no more than a frivolity – but you never know. Perhaps something ghost-like *will* occasionally appear at either side of the railway line during the journey. And maybe one of these appearances will be very soon, before you reach the Grimley Tunnel that Ted mentioned. But in which *direction* do you watch out for it – in the direction of that water mill on the *north* side of the railway line, or that clump of trees on the *south* side? Or should you bother watching in any direction just for the moment? Perhaps you shouldn't expect the ghosts to start appearing until you've at least passed Grimley Tunnel . . .

If you have circled the M in your score card's  *column, you may consult the MAP accessory now to find out whether a ghost is likely to appear before Grimley Tunnel on the outward journey. If not, you'll have to take a risk:*

Watch water mill	*go to 98*
Watch clump of trees	*go to 12*
Don't bother watching here	*go to 42*

Even if Ted doesn't believe that there are ghosts along this railway line, *you* are still a little hopeful that there might be. So you slip into one of the compartments and sit down on the worn upholstery while you check that your camera is all set up to take its next photograph. You've just finished this check when everything suddenly goes dark . . . ***Go to 63.***

127

You feel yourself start to go tense – because you now see that eerie viaduct approaching again! The dark valley looks even worse this time, the bottom completely lost in murky shadow, and you keep your eyes shut as the train puffs slowly across it. If there are any ghosts to be spotted in those spooky depths, you really don't think you care this time! ***Go to 58.***

128

The signal box is right at the end of the platform, beyond where the wooden canopy ends, and so you have to make a dash for it through the rain. You then charge up the dozen or so steps towards the tall hut but you've become wet for nothing. The signal box door is firmly locked! You're hurrying back down again when you suddenly slip on one of the drenched steps. Fortunately you just grab the handrail in time or the slip could have been much more serious. *Unfortunately*, though, you knocked your camera's shutter-release button as you broke your fall!

Delete the top number in your score card's  column. Go next to 104.

129

'Well, if you didn't pull the communication cord, who did?' Ted asks irritably after he has waved his flag out of the window to let the driver know that it was a false alarm. 'Now, yer not going to tell me that it was those ghosts, are you?' But then Ted suddenly notices a strange white powder on the communication cord. He turns rather pale as he examines it. 'W-well, as long as yer not 'urt, that's the main thing,' he says, slightly anxious as he leaves your carriage. **Go to 114.**

130

Looking out of the pull-down window, you can now just make out Mistfield station in the distance. You peer hard for ghosts just before it. But precisely *where* do you watch for them . . . inside the signal box that's now approaching; near that water tank on the opposite side of the line; or on the passenger footbridge just beyond these two?

If you have circled the N in your score card's 🚂
column, you may consult the NEWSPAPER access-
ory now to find out where a ghost will appear on the
outward journey. If not, you'll have to take a risk:

Watch signal box	go to 41
Watch water tank	go to 13
Watch footbridge	go to 71
Don't bother watching here	go to 144

131

You press right against the window on the left side of the carriage, keeping your camera as steady as you can. The billows of steam that suddenly fly past tell you that the engine must now be entering the narrow tunnel. Your finger hovers over your camera's shutter-release button, ready to press it at any moment. Is it your imagination or can you just make out a dancing skeleton amongst all that steam? Unfortunately, you can't wait until the steam disperses a little, for your carriage will have soon passed the 'skeleton' and followed the rest of the train into the tunnel. If you're going to take a photograph, it must be *right now*.

> **If take photo**   go to 14
> **If not**   go to 28

132
Your watch shows that the time is coming up to seven-fifty. You wonder if this is when a ghost is due to appear at one of the train's windows, remembering that Walter Potts had said that they always appeared there at exactly

the same times. But even if the time is right, is this second class carriage the right *place*? If it isn't, then there's no point in watching out for a ghost anyway!

If you have circled the T in your score card's  *column, you may consult the TIMETABLE accessory now to find out if a ghost will appear at this carriage at this time. If not, you'll have to take a risk:*

    Watch your windows   *go to 48*
    Don't bother watching yet   *go to 24*

133

There's also an old newspaper wedged under the weighing-machine! Someone many years back must have accidentally kicked it under the scales – and it has lain there ever since. But how the paper found its way under the machine doesn't really interest you that much. What *really* interests you is the newspaper's headline! The front page story is all about Walter Potts and where he claims to have seen ghosts along the railway line. You decide to take the newspaper with you. Walter Potts was probably just an old crank, of course, but if there *is* anything in his claims about the ghosts, then the details in this newspaper might help you to spot them!

You are now entitled to use the NEWSPAPER accessory. Circle the N in the 📰 column of your score card so that you have a reminder of this whenever the newspaper is required. Go next to 69.

Well risked! You've caught the eerie figure on film. Record this success in the 📷 column of your score card. Also, delete the top number in the 🎞 column to deduct the photo used. Go next to 7.

'That was *your* announcement, wasn't it, Ted?' you ask, seeking confirmation of this as Ted now ambles towards you along the platform. But Ted clearly doesn't know what you're talking about. 'Give us a chance, will you?' he replies. 'That's just what I was going to do. We're at Littleoak station again and we'll be stopping 'ere for some five minutes if you want to 'ave a quick stroll round. There's your announcement for you!' *Go to 113.*

Preparing for when you pass under the footbridge, you kneel down on the carriage floor and point your camera upwards at the window. You don't have to be very hurried about this because the train suddenly stops again. But then it starts to edge forwards once more and the footbridge slowly approaches above you. The bridge is so shrouded in the engine's steam, however, that it's difficult to tell whether there's also a ghost hovering there or not. There *might* just be one amongst the clouds of steam perhaps . . . and a photograph of that steam could make it rather clearer. But just say there wasn't. It would be a precious photograph wasted!

If take photo   **go to 91**
If not   **go to 24**

137

Ted at last reaches your compartment and he mutters at you from the door. 'Found you at last,' he grunts. 'Just thought you'd like to know that we'll be coming to the end of our outward journey fairly soon and arriving at Mistfield station. That's as far as the line goes. After the engine 'as been turned round, we travel back to Bleakwood. That'll be an end to all this silly nonsense. Oh, by the way,' he just remembers as he's about to wander off again, 'thanks for 'elping us with that fallen tree.' You have to admit that you've never before received such a grumpy thankyou! *Go to 51.*

Your camera closely follows the shadowy manor house as it gradually moves across the carriage's wide windows . . . but that ghost you were hoping for doesn't look as if it's going to appear! You decide to take one last look at the house through the viewfinder. As you're changing position at the window, however, your feet suddenly slide out in front of you. Pulling yourself up again, you see that there's a wet leaf on the sole of your shoe! You must have picked it up while you were helping to move that tree. But the leaf isn't all you notice. A photograph is starting to emerge from your camera. You must have knocked its shutter-release . . .

Delete the top number in your score card's
column. Go next to 105.

Stepping into one of the compartments in the second class carriage, you immediately pull down the window and peer out. You're now nearing Dark Valley, the train rumbling towards the beginning of a huge viaduct that spans it. Consisting of a series of tall, eerie arches, this viaduct would seem a perfect haunt for ghosts! So you wonder where you should look as you come up to the massive bridge; do you look to its left side, its right, or directly below it!

If you have circled the N in your score card's  *column, you may consult the NEWSPAPER accessory now to find out if a ghost will appear as the train nears the viaduct on its outward journey. If not, you'll have to take a risk:*

Watch left side	*go to 31*
Watch right side	*go to 115*
Watch below viaduct	*go to 84*
Don't bother watching here	*go to 66*

140

You slowly open the door to the waiting-room, hoping to find perhaps one or two other passengers in there. The small wooden bench is quite empty, though. You have a quick look round to see what else is in the half-dark room. There's just a rusty iron stove, a few yellowing timetables . . . and an old chocolate machine. Although you know it's bound not to work, you can't resist trying the chocolate machine and you tug at its little metal drawer. You were absolutely right – the drawer is firmly jammed! You give the drawer another good tug just in case. This time, a folded sheet of paper slips down from behind the machine. Someone must have hidden it there! *Go to 80.*

141

You keep your eyes on the broad windows. The problem is that there's a lot more steam flying past the observation car now that it's right behind the engine. It's difficult to see whether there's a ghost hovering amongst all that steam or not! After a while, though, the train slows down a little and the steam begins to disperse. Unfortunately, there isn't a ghost amongst it! Not one you can see, anyway. But you wonder if there are some *invisible* ghosts nearby because your camera suddenly seems to take a photograph of its own accord. You're fairly sure it wasn't *you* who pressed the button. But all that really matters, you suppose, is that this picture of nothing is a waste of your precious film!

Delete the top number in your score card's  column. Go next to 85.

142

With camera at the ready, you rather nervously step out into the corridor. You hear that tapping again. But this time it's from behind you, from *inside* the compartment! You're sure you can sense a ghost watching you from there but you're worried that as soon as you turn round to check, it will disappear. So perhaps you shouldn't take time to check. Perhaps you should just suddenly swing round, simultaneously clicking your camera. What if there *isn't* a ghost behind you, though? You'll have wasted a precious photograph on an empty compartment!

If take photo   go to 36
If not   go to 75

143

To your enormous relief, you find that it was just Ted shuffling along the corridor towards you! He has come to tell you that the train will shortly be reaching the end of its outward journey, soon to arrive at Mistfield station. After Ted has left you again to prepare for this arrival, you wonder whether a ghost will take this last chance to appear on the outward journey! *Go to 112.*

144

The moment the train has stopped at the desolate station, the engine is uncoupled from the carriages. It then moves towards an ancient turntable just beyond the platforms so it can be turned round. Ted helps the engine driver with this operation. But the stoker takes a short rest and comes to have a chat with you as you stretch your legs on the platform. *Go to 62.*

The risk was worth taking! Record this success in the 🖼 *column of your score card. Also, delete the top number in the* 📷 *column to deduct the photo used. Go next to 127.*

Go next to 127.

146

Not long after the train has started moving again, you notice an eerie cottage through the observation car's wide windows. It's a few hundred metres to the right of the railway line and is totally dilapidated. If you suddenly saw a ghost appear there, you wouldn't be in the least surprised! But you then spot an equally eerie building some distance to the left of the railway line. This one is much larger; a type of manor house with spooky chimneys. It wouldn't really surprise you to see a ghost walking there either! So which building should you keep your camera focused on?

If you have circled the M in your score card's  *column, you may study the MAP accessory now to find out if a ghost will appear at either of these locations during the outward journey. If not, you'll have to take a risk:*

Watch manor house	*go to 138*
Watch cottage	*go to 65*
Don't bother watching here	*go to 105*

147

'Go anywhere you want,' Ted says gruffly when you have followed him as far as the second class carriage. It's not an open-plan carriage like the modern ones but full of separate compartments. 'If you want to look out for ghosts to the north side of the line, you should sit in one of the compartments,' he says. 'If you want to look out for them to the south side of the line, you're best staying out 'ere in the corridor. Not that there *will* be any ghosts to see, of course,' he mumbles back over his shoulder as he shuffles further along the train towards the first class carriage. 'This trip's all a shameful frivolity if you ask me!' **Go to 125.**

148

You hear a couple of loud hisses from the engine shed – and see another cloud of steam billow out from its darkness – but still the train doesn't emerge. So you decide to have a quick look round the platform on the other side of the railway line. You dash towards the iron footbridge, clambering up its drenched, uncovered steps. Instead of a waiting-room on this much smaller platform, there's just a single bench. The only other things there are a luggage trolley loaded with leather trunks at one end of the covered platform and a rusty weighing-machine at the other. Both these are obviously relics from many years back and have been left there for authenticity. Since there's *still* no sign of the train, you decide to have a closer look at one of these relics. Which do you think will be more interesting?

If luggage trolley   *go to 46*
If weighing-machine   *go to 108*

149

It was just a squirrel! ***Delete the top number in your score card's*** 📷 ***column. Go next to 66.***

150

Ted immediately leaves your carriage again to prepare for the train's arrival at Mistfield station. You soon follow after him – but only as far as the start of the adjoining carriage, just through the connecting door. The windows aren't as wide here, of course, but they're the pull-down types. This will enable you to poke your head right out as the train approaches the station – just in case there are any ghosts along this final part of the track! *Go to 130.*

151

You at last force yourself to turn slowly round. You let out a huge sigh of relief. It wasn't a ghost that tapped your shoulder – just Ted! 'I forgot to punch yer ticket,' he says, looking rather puzzled by your strange behaviour. 'As if I don't 'ave enough walking to do,' he grumbles, 'without 'aving to come all this way back again!' You have *far* more to complain about, though. Not only did Ted half frighten you to death when he tapped your shoulder, but you now find out that he made you accidentally press the shutter-release button on your camera as well!

Delete the top number in your score card's 📷 *column. Go next to 42.*

You haven't left the tunnel far behind when a ghost suddenly appears right at the train's window! At least, you thought it was a ghost but then you realise that it was just the reflection of one of the electric flashes from the train's power pick-up. Wait a minute, though . . . a steam train wouldn't have a power pick-up! It must have been a ghost after all! But then you hear a deep rumble from the grim countryside all around you. A thunderstorm has started. So that flash was obviously just lightning. What a relief! *Go to 122.*

Before settling in this second class compartment you pull the window right down. It's almost too murky for taking photographs as it is, without this grimy glass in the way! As the train now jerks out of the station, you make an anxious assessment of the current state of the sky. It's just about light enough at the moment, you suppose, but this surely won't last for more than about fifteen minutes. Not unless the rain eases quite a bit. And if it becomes any heavier, you won't even have *five* minutes left for taking photographs! *Go to 15.*

154

A few minutes after the train has started moving again, you hear soft footsteps echoing towards you along the corridor. For a moment you wonder whether they might belong to the ghost of Walter Potts! The footsteps sound very slow and unwilling, though, and you doubt that Walter Potts – even Walter Potts's ghost! – would have as reluctant a walk as this. For all the hauntings he had experienced, he sounded a very jaunty man in the various bits and pieces you'd read about him. No, there is only one person that such dragging footsteps could belong to . . . and that is Ted!
Go to 137.

155

The viaduct's black, sombre arches come nearer and nearer, looking even more eerie than they did before. There might not have been ghosts hanging round the massive bridge last time but you could certainly imagine there would be *this* time! So where do you direct your camera when the train starts to cross the viaduct – towards its left wall, its right wall or straight downwards into the valley?

If you have circled the N in your score card's  *column, you may consult the NEWSPAPER accessory now to find out where a ghost will appear as the train crosses the viaduct on the return journey. If not, you'll have to take a risk:*

Watch left side	*go to 120*
Watch right side	*go to 23*
Watch straight downwards	*go to 52*
Don't bother watching here	*go to 7*

156

You hold your camera up to your eye by the compartment window, waiting for the road bridge to appear in its viewfinder. You can soon see it in the tiny square and you nudge the viewfinder towards those dark, over-grown bushes which climb up its left bank. There's quite a lot of rustling in the eerie foliage and you tensely place your finger on the camera's shutter button in case this is a sign that a ghost is about to materialise there! *Go to 93.*

157

You move over to the right side of the carriage, holding your camera as near to the window as possible. This means you shouldn't have any reflection in your photograph – as long as the carriage lights don't suddenly come on as you enter the tunnel, that is! The tunnel now appears ahead, though, and fortunately the carriage lights remain off as your train comes nearer and nearer to it. If there *is* a ghost hovering there, then you should obtain a clear photo of it. And it looks as if there *might* possibly be one! For you suddenly notice something rather strange. What's that white shape floating at the right side of the tunnel entrance? Could it really be a ghost – or is it just the engine's steam billowing backwards as it enters the tunnel? You can't waste time debating it, though. If you're going to take a photograph, it must be right now!

If take photo go to 44
If not go to 28

If take photo   *go to 44*
If not   *go to 28*

158

It was a ghost. Well done! Record this success in the ☺ *column of your score card. Also, delete the top number in the* 📷 *column to deduct the photo used. Go next to 57.*

'Yes, that's Dark Valley coming up,' Ted confirms with a grunt when you have found him. He's replenishing the supply of paper towels in the train's one washroom. 'Now don't ask me if yer likely to see any ghosts there, because you ain't. I know it's a very dark valley and it can by all accounts be quite a sinister one when yer crossing it at this time of the evening – but that's all there is to it. *I've* never seen a ghost down in the valley and nor do I expect to!' You refuse to let Ted dampen your hopes, though. You're confident that you could take some spooky photos as you cross Dark Valley and you quickly consider which would be the best part of the train to snap them . . .

First class carriage	*go to 45*
Second class carriage	*go to 139*
Observation car	*go to 101*

160

'Used to work on this line in its proper days, all them years ago,' the guard informs you after you have taken your seat on the train and he has told you his name is

Ted. 'Little more than a lad then, of course. And don't ask me if I saw any ghosts then because I didn't. I only worked in the day, mind, but I knew that Walter Potts a bit and I thought 'e was a right crackpot!' The train now starts to move, jolting slowly out of the station and into the greying countryside. This hour – it's just gone seven by your watch – would normally still be very light at this time of the year but the heavy rain has made it almost like dusk already. You hope the sky doesn't grow too much darker or any photographs you take are likely to be underexposed! *Go to 54.*

161

Fortunately, the train travels quite slowly while it's on the viaduct, and so you're given a good few minutes to observe the little stone bridge. It doesn't really make any difference, though. No ghost suddenly appears down there. Just as the stone bridge is beginning to disappear from your sight, however, you notice something white float up from under its arches. It now seems to be flying along the river towards the viaduct! Ideally, you'd like to wait until it's a little nearer, but the river will be hidden completely at any moment and so you mustn't delay. If a photograph is to be taken, it must be immediately!

If take photo   **go to 16**
If not   **go to 75**

162
Opening the notebook, you see that every page is empty except the middle two pages. When you start to read what has been jotted down here, you can barely contain your excitement. The double page is headed *Timetable of ghost appearances at carriage windows* and underneath are listed the exact times of all these appearances. And the locations as well – whether they were in the first class or second class carriages or in the observation car! How the notebook ended up in the coal scuttle you simply

can't guess. But there's one thing you're fairly sure about it. The notes were jotted down by Walter Potts!

You are now entitled to use the TIMETABLE accessory. Circle the T in your score card's  column so that you have a reminder of this whenever the timetable is required. Go to 104.

163

You step into the corridor and pull down one of the windows there as well so you have a much clearer view of the farmhouse. Yes, there's absolutely no doubt now that that's what the building is. What you're less sure about, though, is that whitish mist hovering above the chimney of the farmhouse. Is it just smoke wafting out of the chimney – or is it a *ghost*? After all, it's the middle of summer. It might be a very stormy day but it's not really cold enough for someone to light a fire! So perhaps you should quickly photograph this farmhouse before you're too far past it. It might make the ghost a bit clearer . . .

> *If take photo*   go to 6
> *If not*   go to 24

164

Just as you're popping your head into the very last compartment, everything suddenly goes dark. The train must have entered the Grimley Tunnel that Ted had mentioned. You wonder why the carriage lights don't go on – but then you realise that it's probably intentional that they don't go on so the tunnel is given more atmosphere! It's atmosphere that you could really do without, though, and you grope your way to the nearest seat, waiting for the eerie tunnel to end. At last it looks as if it *is* coming to an end as a small patch of light now appears ahead. *Go to 152.*

165

You've just sat down in one of the first class compartments when, with a scream and a jolt, the train starts to move out of the station. As it gradually picks up speed, you lower the rattling window to give yourself as good a view as possible again. For the first few minutes it's still very dark outside – far too dark to take any photographs – but then the storm turns the sky a more yellowy colour. The passing hills and trees still look very shadowy and eerie under that sky but at least they've lightened quite a bit! *Go to 79.*

Collect all six titles in this series:

And have you also read Stephen Thraves' Super Adventure Game Books with separate cards and special dice?